OH MONSTER TRUCK, I'M POTTY TRAINED

By
Chandler & Amiyra King

ALSO BY

CHANDLER & AMIYRA KING

Oh Monster Truck, Come Sleep With Me

DEDICATION:

This book is dedicated to all Monster Truck lovers and their Amazing
parents needing an extra push to get their big boy to potty train.

Today's the big day.

It's my special day!

I turn three years old and I'm ready to play.

I jump out of bed and grab my monster truck.

No more pull-ups or sippy cups!

I see a new potty in the bathroom.

It is small, green, and white, just like the colors of my bike.

Mom and Dad brought in stickers to make it all mine.

I added stickers to my potty and shared some with Monster Truck.

At first, I was scared.

I didn't want to go near the new potty.

Then, I tried again; this time, with my special friend, Monster Truck.

I couldn't believe what I saw!

It wasn't scary at all!

Daddy came to help me.

Then, we washed our hands.

Counting to twenty is always part of the plan.

Being a big boy is oh so fun!

I know my colors, shapes, days, and months.

I'm still learning my letters and all their sounds!

I can't wait to potty all on my own.

Just after a few tries,

I have more high-fives and stickers nearby!

Hooray! Hooray!

Oh, Monster Truck, we did it!

Oh, Monster Truck, I'm potty trained!

Now, color your big boy potty and monster truck!

ABOUT THE AUTHOR

Chandler Jarrod King is a thriving three year old who loves to create books he wishes to see, with the help of his mom, Amiyra King. After seeing his first book, Oh Monster Truck Come Sleep With Me, Chandler wanted much more.

At Journal Joy, LLC , we strive to create a love for literacy in every child; and in turn, change that love to create their own books.

You can purchase additional books from the author at www.thejournaljoy.com and all major retailers and bookstores.